Mandalas
for Mindfulness

igloobooks

Published in 2018
by Igloo Books Ltd
Cottage Farm
Sywell
NN6 0BJ
www.igloobooks.com

Designed by Charles Wood-Penn
Edited by Vicky Taylor

Interiors illustrated by Ashish Dhir
All other images: iStock

VIV001 0318
6 8 10 9 7
ISBN: 978-1-78557-421-4

Printed and manufactured in Malaysia

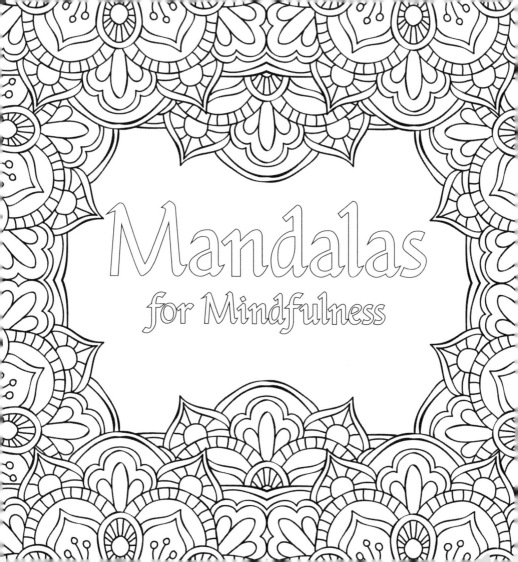

Mandalas

for Mindfulness

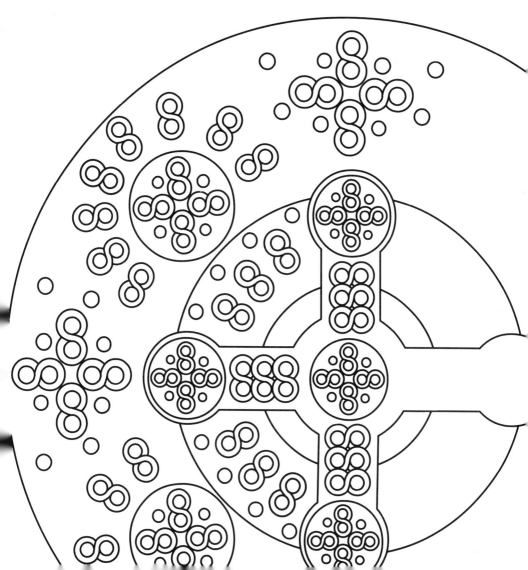

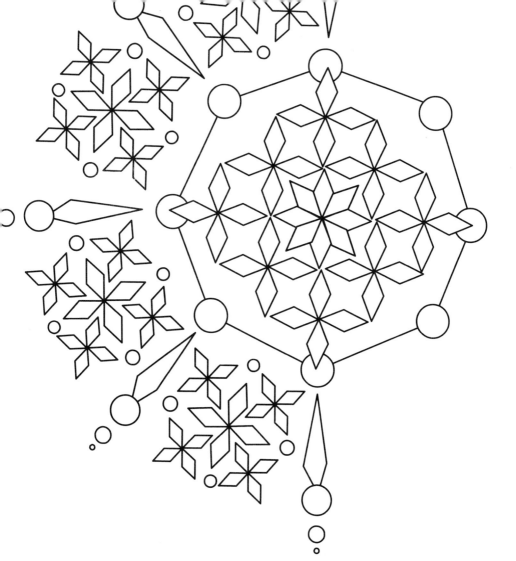

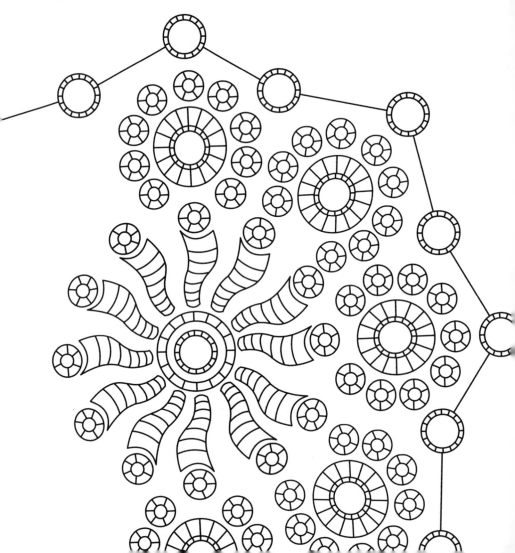

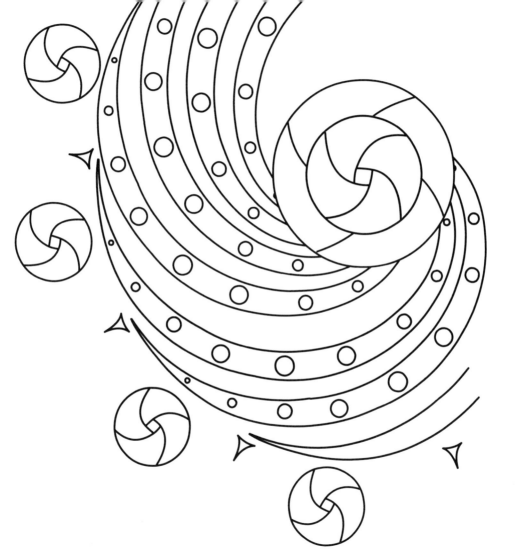

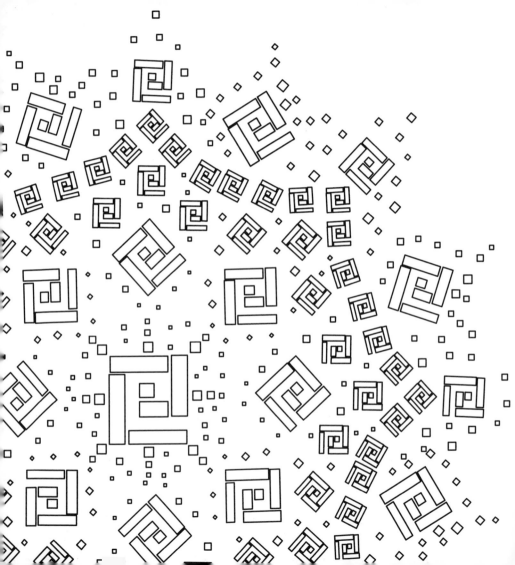

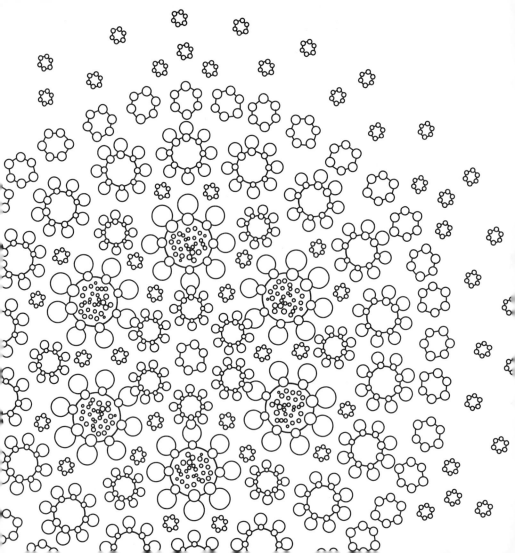

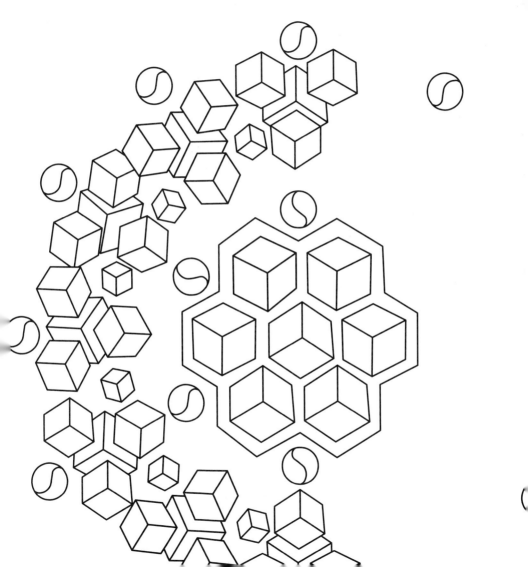

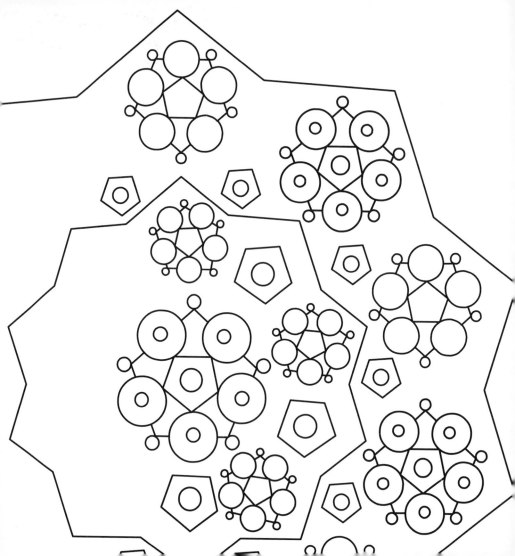

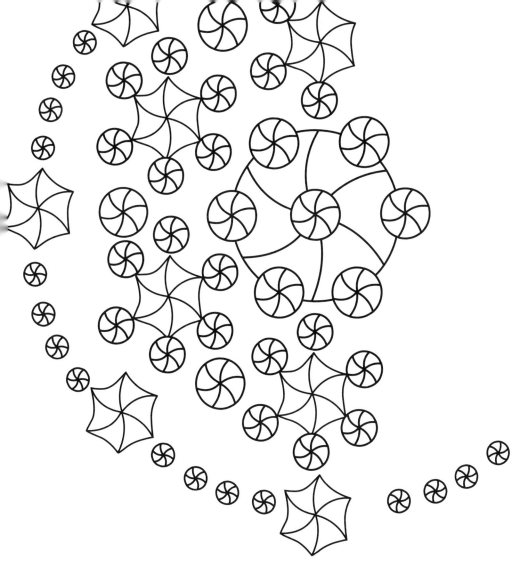

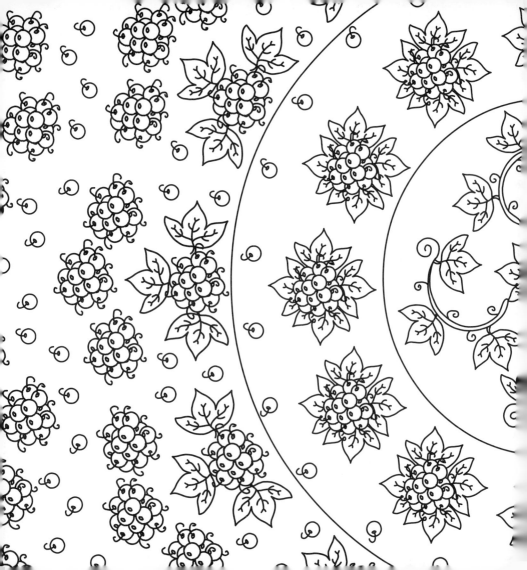

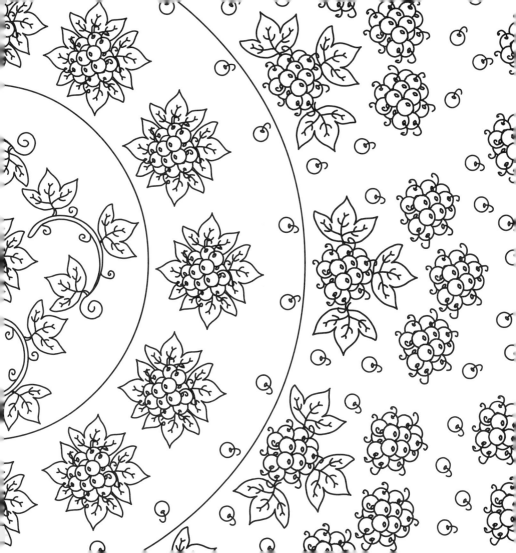

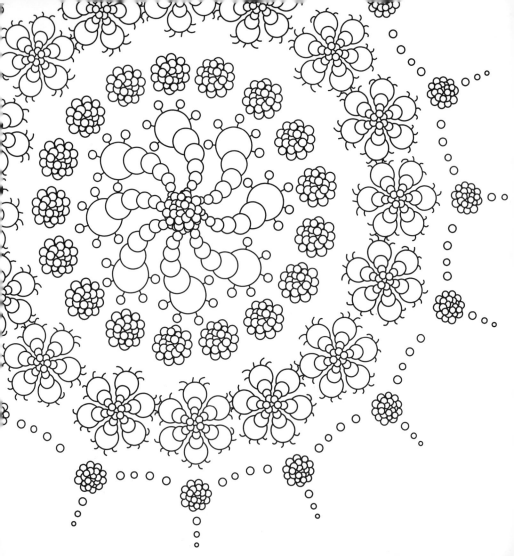

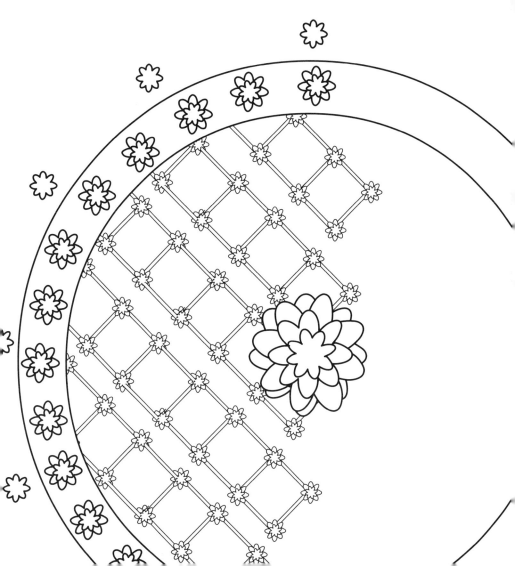

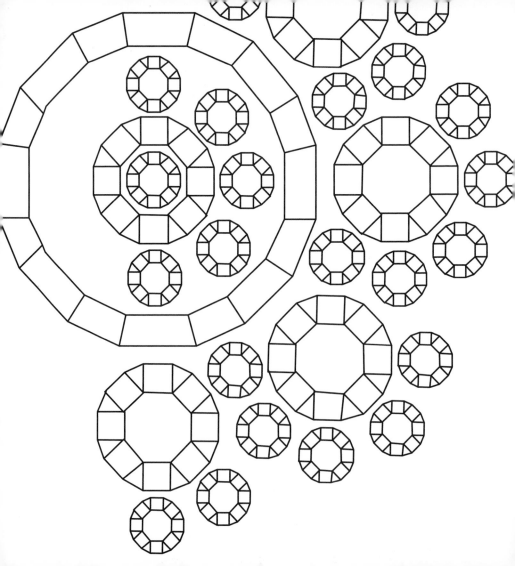

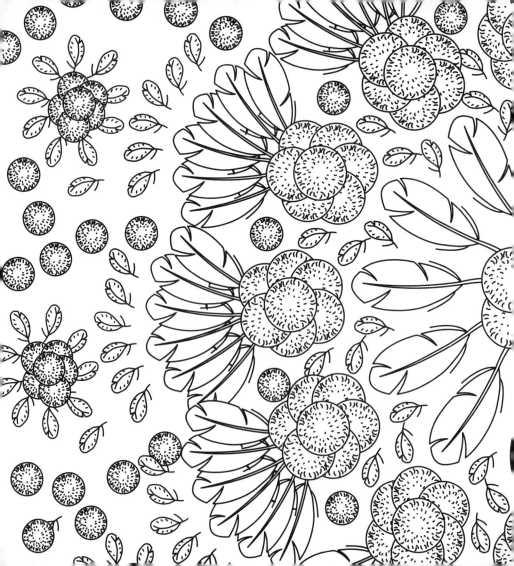

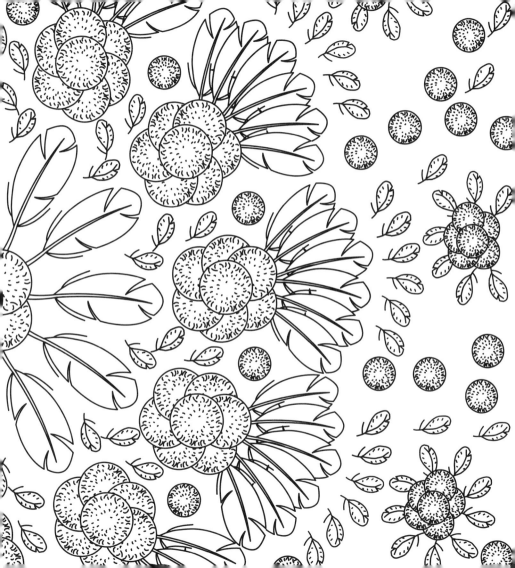

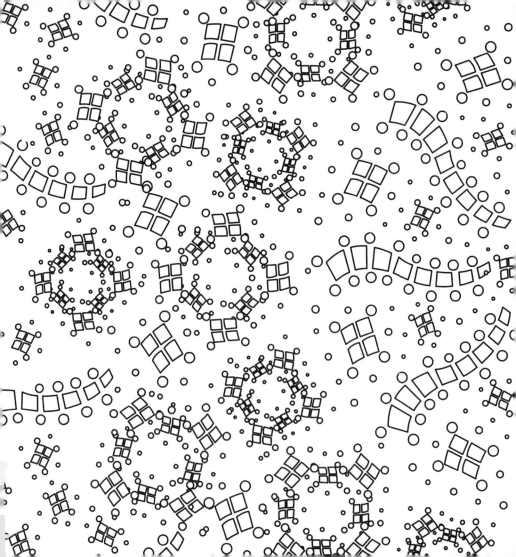

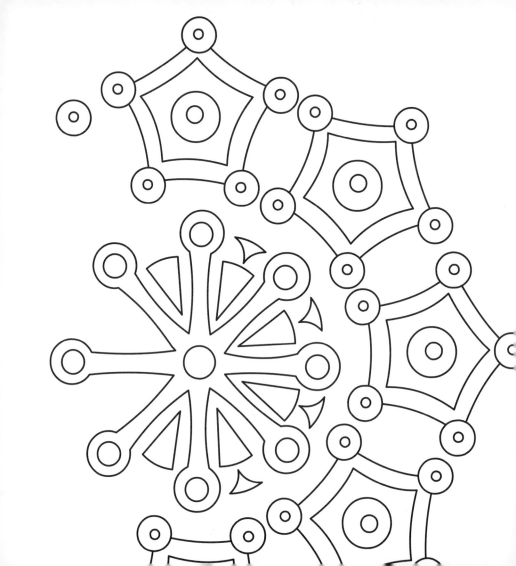

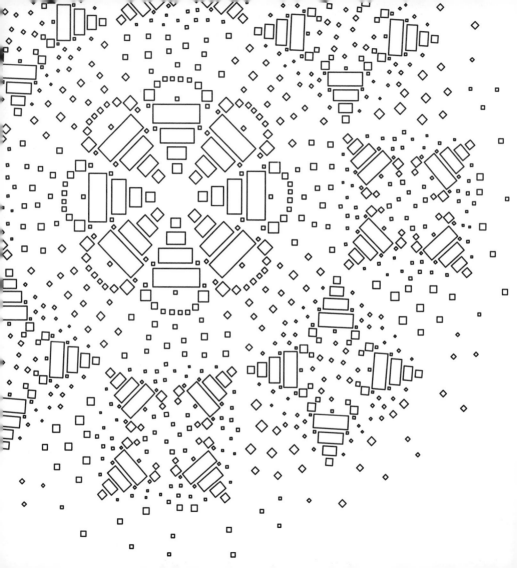

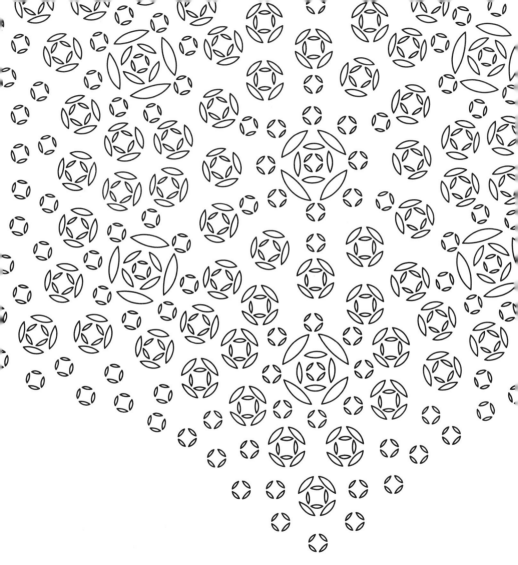

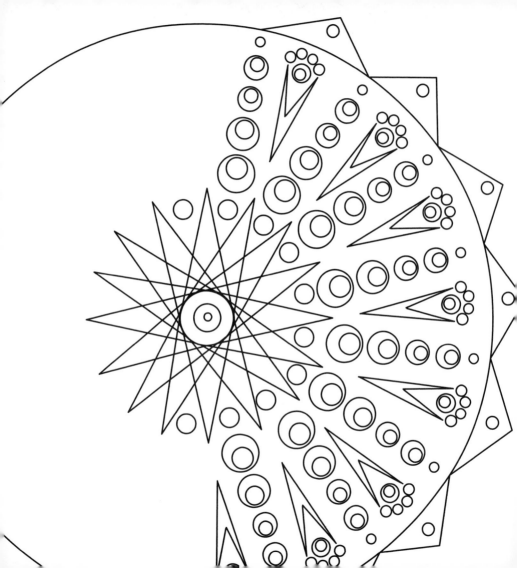

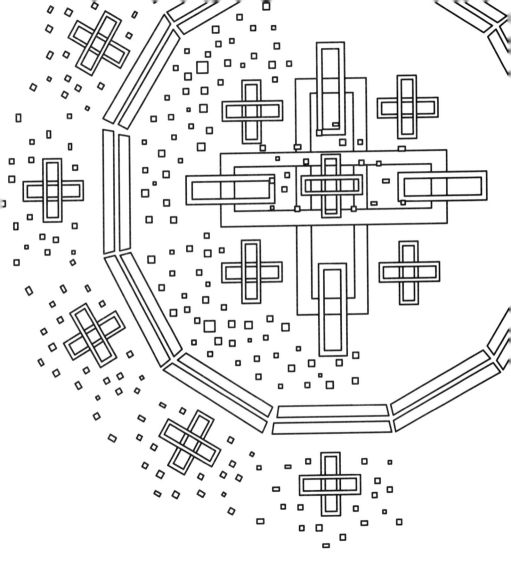

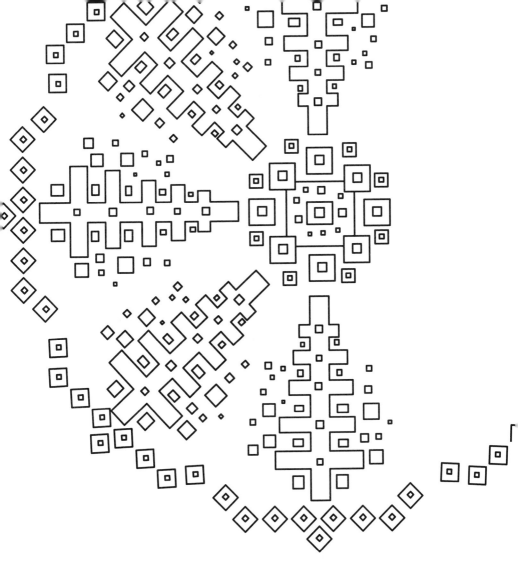